This Book Belongs To

_____

COPYRIGHT © 2006 Nanci Bell
Gander Publishing
412 Higuera Street, Suite 200
San Luis Obispo, CA 93401
805-541-5523 • 800-554-1819
ISBN 0-945856-49-0

VISUALIZING AND VERBALIZING AND V/V ARE REGISTERED TRADEMARKS OF NANCI BELL.

Overview and Directions

This workbook is designed to develop gestalt imagery and language comprehension with the Visualizing and Verbalizing for Language Comprehension and Thinking® (V/V®) Program.

Following the steps of V/V®, detail and gestalt imagery are developed with Sentence by Sentence, Multiple Sentence, Whole Paragraph, and Paragraph by Paragraph V/V® stimulation.

Each story is high in imagery and followed by these workbook activities:

- Imagery Questions
- Word Summary
- Main Idea
- Higher Order Thinking Skills (HOTS)

As the student begins each story, he/she should decode the vocabulary words and visualize the meaning. This will help create imagery and develop contextual fluency. There are different types of imagery questions. The student should either underline an answer or fill in the blank. The student may write a single word or phrase in the blank to describe his/her imagery.

These workbooks have been written specifically to help students learn and discover the wonder of the written word by improving gestalt imagery, critical thinking, and writing skills. Once these skills are developed, the possibilities are endless.

Remember, you can help students do this. You can do anything!

Nanci Bell
2006

Meet Ivan!

I am Ivan, King of the Neighborhood. I'm big and wide and full of pride!

I **love** to eat!

I **love** to sleep!

I am a cat!

1 The One That Got Away

The cat crouches in the backyard staring at a small lizard on a nearby rock. In a flash, the cat pounces. He grabs the lizard's tail with his teeth. The lizard sheds its tail and runs away.

Vocabulary to Visualize:

crouch: to get close to the ground
lizard: a small reptile with a body covered in scales and a long tail
pounce: to jump on suddenly
shed: to get rid of

Picture This: The cat crouches in the backyard staring at a small lizard on a nearby rock. In a flash, the cat pounces.

Underline or write in the answer that best matches your own picture.

1. What did those words make you picture?   cat hunting   lizard hunting

2. How did you picture the cat hunting?   cat jumping on lizard   lizard jumping on cat

3. How did you see the cat staring?   eyes open   eyes closed

4. What did you see the cat staring at?   lizard   rock   grass

5. Where did you see the lizard?   on a rock   in the grass   in a tree

6. How did you picture the cat pouncing?   jumping fast   falling down

7. What did you picture the cat jumping on?   a rock   a lizard   a tree

8. What color did you picture the cat? _____

9. What color did you picture the lizard? _____

B **Picture This:** He grabs the lizard's tail with his teeth. The lizard sheds its tail and runs away.

Underline the answer that best matches your own picture.

1. What did those words make you picture?   lizard gets away   lizard is trapped

2. How did you see the lizard getting away?   lizard runs away from cat   lizard bumps into cat

3. Where did you see the cat grabbing the lizard?   on the tail   on the leg

4. Where did you picture the lizard's tail?   in the cat's mouth   under the rock

5. How did you picture the lizard shedding its tail?   tail coming off   tail staying on

6. How did you see the lizard running?   fast   slow

7. What did you see for the lizard's mood?   sad   scared   happy

Picture Summary:

Put these in the right order. Draw a picture if you want.

The cat jumped on the lizard and bit down on its tail.	A cat looked at a lizard.	The lizard let go of its tail and ran away from the cat.

5

Word Summary:
Fill in the blanks using the words listed below.

The _____ looked at a lizard on a rock. The

cat _____. He bit and held onto the lizard's

_____ . The tail came off and the lizard

_____ away.

ran   **tail**   **cat**   **jumped**

Main Idea:
Connect these with a line.

A lizard tried to catch a cat.	a detail
A cat tried to catch a lizard.	main idea
A lizard sat on a rock.	wrong

Spelling Practice:
Trace then cover the word.   Air-write then pencil write the word.

staring

grabs

Vocabulary Check:
Draw a line from the word to its meaning.

crouch	a small reptile, covered in scales
lizard	to jump on suddenly
pounce	to get rid of
shed	get close to the ground
nearby	next to; close to

HOTS Questions:

1. What do you think will happen next?_____

_____

2. Why do you think the cat tried to catch the lizard?_____

_____

3. How do you think the cat felt when the lizard got away?_____

_____

4. How do you think the lizard felt when he got away?_____

_____

Vocabulary Fun:

Color the picture that best matches the word.

crouch   **lizard**   **backyard**

2 The Clown Show

In the dressing room, Jim put on his huge red pants and big shoes. He painted his face white with a big red smile. He put on a giant bow tie and a wig. When the music began, Jim ran out on the stage and tripped over his big shoes.

Vocabulary to Visualize:

bow tie: a short tie, in a bow
wig: fake hair worn on the head
stage: a place where actors perform
trip: to fall

Picture This: In the dressing room, Jim put on his huge red pants and big shoes. He painted his face white with a big red smile.

Underline or write in the answer that best matches your own picture.

1. What did those words make you picture?   Jim dresses as a clown   Jim dresses as a cat

2. How did you see Jim dressing as a clown?   put on funny clothes   put on fur coat

3. What color did you see his pants? _____

4. What color did you picture his big shoes? _____

5. What did you see him paint on his face?   a smile   a frown   tear drops

6. How did you picture the dressing room?   room with a mirror   stage with people

7. How did you see his pants?   tight   baggy

8. How old did you picture Jim?   young boy   young man   old man

B **Picture This:** He put on a giant bow tie and a wig. When the music began, Jim ran out on the stage and tripped over his big shoes.

Underline or write in the answer that best matches your own picture.

1. What did those words make you picture?   Jim starting his show   Jim singing

2. How did you picture Jim starting his show?   going on stage   running into street

3. What did you see Jim do before going onstage?   finished getting ready   ate some popcorn

4. What did you see for Jim's wig?   flat hair   curly hair

5. What color did you see Jim's giant bow? _____

6. What did you see Jim do when he heard the music start?   run on stage   go home

7. What did you see Jim do when he tripped?   fell down hard   fell on cat

Picture Summary:

Put these in the right order. Draw a picture if you want.

Jim ran out on stage and tripped over his shoes.	Jim put on a bow tie, and a wig.	Jim put on pants, and shoes and then painted his face.

Word Summary:
Fill in the blanks using the words listed below.

Jim put on big _____ and shoes in a dressing

room. He put a red smile on his _____ face.

He put a _____ on his head and a big bow tie

around his neck. When he heard the music, he ran on

_____ and tripped.

wig   **white**   **stage**   **pants**

Main Idea:
Connect these with a line.

Jim dressed up as a clown to put on a show.	a detail
Jim went to watch a clown show.	main idea
Jim painted a smile on his face.	wrong

Spelling Practice:
Trace then cover the word.   Air-write then pencil write the word.

music

tripped

Vocabulary Check:
Draw a line from the word to its meaning.

clown	fake hair worn on the head
bow tie	an actor who wears silly costumes
wig	to fall
stage	a short tie, in a bow
trip	a place where actors perform

HOTS Questions:

1. What do you think happened next?_____

_____

2. Do you think Jim wanted to look serious or funny? Why?_____

_____

3. Why do you think Jim tripped?_____

_____

4. Do you think Jim meant to trip? _____

_____

Vocabulary Fun:

Color the picture that best matches the word.

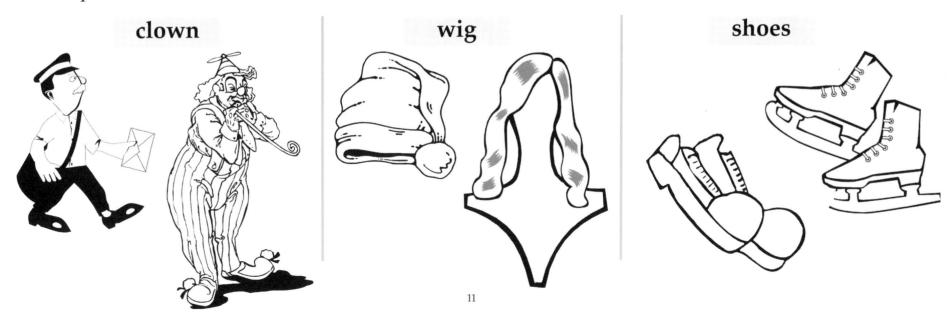

clown   wig   shoes

3 Ferrets

Ferrets are fun pets that like to explore. They squirm in and out of desk drawers. They open latched doors where their food is kept and eat it all. They lift the lids of hampers and nose through the dirty clothes.

Vocabulary to Visualize:

ferret: animal with short legs, a long thin body, and a tail
explore: look around in new places
squirm: to move by twisting and turning
latched: closed with a piece of metal or wood
hamper: a bin that holds dirty clothes

Picture This: Ferrets are fun pets that like to explore. They squirm in and out of desk drawers.

Underline the answer that best matches your own picture.

1. What did those words make you picture?	ferrets playing around a house	ferrets sleeping all day
2. How did you see the ferrets as fun?	sobbing sleeping	playing
3. How did you picture them exploring?	running all around	staying in one spot
4. How did you see that the ferrets are pets?	they live in a house	they live in the woods
5. What did you picture in the desk drawer?	pens and markers	clothes food
6. How did you see them squirm into the drawer?	open it with their paws	squeeze into the open drawer
7. What did you see them doing in the desk?	sleeping writing	chewing on pens
8. How did you picture them going in and out?	popping their heads out and in	falling off the desk

B **Picture This:** They open latched doors where their food is kept and eat it all. They lift the lids of hampers and nose through the dirty clothes.

Underline the answer that best matches your own picture.

1. What did those words make you picture?   ferrets exploring more places   ferrets sleeping more

2. Where did you see them exploring now?   in cupboards and hampers   in trash cans and showers

3. Where did you picture the door with their food?   in the kitchen   in the bathroom

4. How did you picture them after they ate?   fat and full   skinny and hungry

5. Where did you picture the hamper?   in the kitchen   in the bathroom   in the closet

6. How did you see them get in the hamper?   climb up and in   chew through the side

7. How did you picture the dirty clothes?   neatly folded   wrinkled and crumpled

Picture Summary:

Put these in the right order. Draw a picture if you want.

Ferrets got into their food and ate it all.	Ferrets opened a hamper and went through the dirty clothes.	Ferrets wiggled in and out of a desk drawer.

Word Summary:
Fill in the blanks using the words listed below.

Ferrets like to explore and _____ . They like
to squeeze in and _____ of drawers. They
open doors to get _____ and eat it all. They
like to get into the _____ clothes and play.

out   **play**   **dirty**   **food**

Main Idea:
Connect these with a line.

Ferrets hate playing and would rather sleep all day.		a detail
Ferrets eat all their food.		main idea
Ferrets are fun and like to explore.		wrong

Spelling Practice:
Trace then cover the word.

Air-write then pencil write the word.

explore

dirty

Vocabulary Check:
Draw a line from the word to its meaning.

ferret	closed with a piece of metal or wood
explore	to move by twisting and turning
squirm	a basket that holds dirty clothes
latched	to look around in new places
hamper	animal with long thin body

HOTS Questions:

1. Do you think it would be fun to own a ferret? Why or why not? _____

_____

2. How smart do you think a ferret is? _____

_____

3. How do you think he opens latched doors? _____

_____

4. Where else do you think a ferret might go? _____

_____

Vocabulary Fun:

Color the picture that best matches the word.

ferret	drawer	hamper

 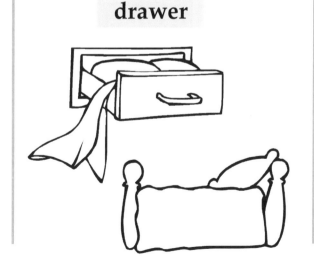  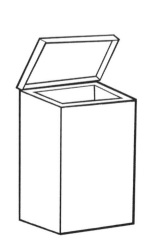

4 The Llama

The llama lives high up in the snowy mountains. His thick brown fur helps keep him warm. He loves to eat the shrubs and grass that he finds near rocks. If another llama gets too close, he will spit on it.

Vocabulary to Visualize:

llama: an animal that looks like a camel without a hump
fur: thick hair on an animal that can be short or long
shrub: any woody plant with no trunk but lots of stems

Picture This: The llama lives high up in the snowy mountains. His thick brown fur helps keep him warm.

Underline or write in the answer that best matches your own picture.

1. What did those words make you picture? a llama living in cold a llama on the beach

2. Where did you picture the llama living? on a mountain in water

3. How did you see it living in snow? always in snow always on the beach

4. What color did you see the snow? _____

5. What did you see for high in the snowy mountains? top of mountain bottom of mountain

6. What color did you picture his thick fur? _____

7. How did you see his thick fur? lots of hair very little hair

8. How did you see that the llama is warm? shivering not shivering

B **Picture This:** He loves to eat the shrubs and grass that he finds near rocks. If another llama gets too close, he will spit on it.

Underline or write in the answer that best matches your own picture.

1. What did those words make you picture?　　llama eating and spitting　　llama sleeping

2. What did you see the llama eating?　　plants　　shoes

3. How did you see the llama eating the plants?　　pulling with mouth　　pulling with hooves

4. How did you see the plants?　　growing next to rocks　　growing on top of rocks

5. How did you see that the other llama was close?　　standing next to him　　standing far away

6. What color did you picture the other llama? _____

7. Where did you see the llama spit?　　on the ground　　on the other llama

Picture Summary:

Put these in the right order. Draw a picture if you want.

The llama spit on another llama.	A llama with brown fur stood in the snow on a mountain.	The llama ate grass and bushes.

Word Summary:

Fill in the blanks using the words listed below.

A llama _____ up in the mountains. His

_____ helps keep him warm. He eats

_____ and grass. He will _____

on things that get too close.

spit   **fur**   **lives**   **bushes**

Main Idea:

Connect these with a line.

A llama spits.	a detail
Animals have fur.	main idea
All about the llama.	wrong

Spelling Practice:

Trace then cover the word.   Air-write then pencil write the word.

high

snowy

Vocabulary Check:

Draw a line from the word to its meaning.

llama	an animal that looks like a camel
mountain	thick hair on an animal
fur	a woody plant with no trunk
shrub	covered with snow
snowy	a tall rocky place

HOTS Questions:

1. Why do you think it might be good for the llama to have thick fur? _____

_____

2. What do you think might happen if the llama had short fur? _____

_____

3. Do you think shrubs and grass are easy for the llama to find? Why? _____

_____

4. Would you want to stand close to a llama? Why or why not? _____

_____

Vocabulary Fun:

Color the picture that best matches the word.

llama

shrub

spit

19

Slow Poke

In Spain, a herd of bulls in a small pen wait for the gate to open. A rocket is fired, the gate opens, and all the bulls run down the streets to the stadium. People try to run in front of the bulls to show they are brave. Some do not run fast enough. Ouch!

Vocabulary to Visualize:

Spain: a country in Europe
herd: a group of animals
pen: a fenced-in place for animals
rocket: a firework
stadium: a place where sports are played, with lots of seats for people to watch
brave: being able to do something even when afraid

A **Picture This:** In Spain, a herd of bulls in a small pen wait for the gate to open. A rocket is fired, the gate opens, and all the bulls run down the streets to the stadium.

Underline the answer that best matches your own picture.

1. What did those words make you picture?   bulls running in a city   bulls sleeping in a field

2. How did you see the bulls being let into the city?   let out of a pen   fell from the sky

3. What did you see on the bull's head?   sharp horns   long soft ears   feathers

4. How big did you picture the pen?   bulls spread out   bulls squeezed together

5. What did you hear for the rocket?   loud boom   soft beep

6. How did you see the gate open?   swings slowly   swings quickly

7. How did you see the bulls running?   slow   fast

8. Where in the street did you see the bulls running?   on the road   into houses

9. How big did you see the stadium?   big as a dog house   big as a baseball field

B **Picture This:** People try to run in front of the bulls to show they are brave. Some do not run fast enough. Ouch!

Underline the answer that best matches your own picture.

1. What did those words make you picture?   bulls running alone   people running with bulls

2. How did you see people running with bulls?   running in the same street   riding the bulls

3. Where do you picture people running?   in front of the bulls   on the rooftops

4. How do you see people in front of bulls?   near the bull's face and horns   near the bull's tail

5. How did you see people showing they are brave?   close to bulls   far away from bulls

6. How do you see people not running fast enough?   people getting hurt   people getting away

7. How do you see people getting hurt?   people getting caught by horns   bulls getting hurt

Picture Summary:
Put these in the right order. Draw a picture if you want.

A gate opened and the bulls ran out of the pen into the streets.	A bunch of bulls waited in a pen until a rocket went off.	People ran in front of the bulls to the stadium.

Word Summary:

Fill in the blanks using the words listed below.

Bulls _____ in a pen. When the gate opens,

the _____ run wildly down the

_____ . The people try to stay in

_____ of the bulls. Some people get

crushed by the big bulls.

bulls   street   wait   front

Main Idea:

Connect these with a line.

People run with bulls in the streets of Spain.	a detail
People ride the bulls in the streets of Spain.	main idea
When the rocket fires, the gate opens.	wrong

Spelling Practice:

Trace then cover the word.   Air-write then pencil write the word.

street

enough

Vocabulary Check:

Draw a line from the word to its meaning.

Spain	a firework
rocket	a place where sports are played
pen	a country in Europe
herd	a fenced in place for animals
stadium	a group of animals

HOTS Questions:

1. What do you think happens to the people who don't run fast enough? _____

_____

2. Why do you think the bulls are going to the stadium? _____

_____

3. Why do you think people would want to run in front of bulls? _____

_____

4. Do you think it would be fun to run with the bulls? Why or why not? _____

_____

Vocabulary Fun:

Color the picture that best matches the word.

bull   **herd**   **stadium**

6 Swoop For Supper

The gray and white falcon soaring in the clouds saw a bird flying near the ground. He tucked his wings in and zoomed straight down at the other bird. With his talons, he struck the bird's back. The wounded bird died before it hit the ground.

Vocabulary to Visualize:

falcon: a hawk-like bird that is the fastest in the world
soar: to fly high in the air
zoom: to move very fast
talon: a hooked claw on the toe of a bird
wound: to hurt badly

A **Picture This:** The gray and white falcon soaring in the clouds saw a bird flying near the ground. He tucked his wings in and zoomed straight down at the other bird.

Underline or write in the answer that best matches your own picture.

1. What did those words make you picture?   a falcon hunting   a falcon swimming

2. What did you picture the falcon hunting?   another bird   a mouse

3. Where did you see the falcon hunting?   high in the sky   on the ground

4. Where did you see the other bird flying?   near the ground   as high as clouds

5. How did you see the falcon tuck his wings?   pull them in   stretch them out

6. How did you picture him zooming?   flying really fast   flying really slow

7. How did you picture him going straight down?   like an arrow   like a rainbow

8. What did you see the falcon flying at?   the other bird   a fish

9. What colors did you picture the falcon? _____ and _____

24

B **Picture This:** With his talons, he struck the bird's back. The wounded bird died before it hit the ground.

Underline the answer that best matches your own picture.

1. What did those words make you picture?   falcon killing bird   bird killing falcon

2. How did you see the falcon killing the other bird?   falcon hits bird   falcon misses bird

3. Where did you see the falcon hitting the other bird?   in the back   in the belly

4. What did you see for the talons?   feet with claws   wings with feathers

5. What did you see the hurt bird doing?   flying in sky   falling from sky

6. Where did you picture the dead bird landing?   on the ground   in the water

Picture Summary:

Put these in the right order. Draw a picture if you want.

A falcon flew high in the sky and saw another bird below it.	The falcon flew down and struck the other bird.	The other bird died and fell to the ground.

Word Summary:

Fill in the blanks using the words listed below.

A falcon sees a _____ below it. The falcon

flies really _____ down at the other bird.

The falcon_____ the bird. The bird falls to

the _____ .

hits   **bird**   **fast**   **ground**

Main Idea:

Connect these with a line.

The falcon is gray and white.	a detail
A bird hunts a falcon.	main idea
A falcon hunts another bird.	wrong

Spelling Practice:

Trace then cover the word.   Air-write then pencil write the word.

flying

ground

Vocabulary Check:

Draw a line from the word to its meaning.

falcon	to move very fast
zoom	to hurt badly
talon	to fly high
soar	a hawk-like bird
wound	a hooked claw on the toe of a bird

HOTS Questions:

1. What do you think happened next? _____

_____

2. Why do you think it is important the falcon zooms at his prey? _____

_____

3. Do you think this hurts the falcon? _____

_____

4. Would you want a falcon? Why? _____

_____

Vocabulary Fun:

Color the picture that best matches the word.

falcon	**soaring**	**talon**

  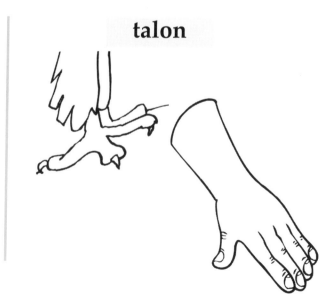

7 Tree House

The father and son hauled wood, a hammer, and nails up a ladder into the tree. They built a floor, four walls, and a roof. They brought up flashlights and a radio. Then they unrolled their sleeping bags and stayed in the tree house all night.

Vocabulary to Visualize:

haul: to carry something heavy
hammer: a tool used to pound things
nail: a small metal pin with a flat, round top
built: made

A **Picture This:** The father and son hauled wood, a hammer, and nails up a ladder into the tree. They built a floor, four walls, and a roof.

Underline or write in the answer that best matches your own picture.

1. What did those words make you picture? building a tree house cutting down a tree

2. Where did you see them building it? in a tree in a bush in a pool

3. Where did you picture the tree? in the back yard in the front yard in a forest

4. How did you see them haul their wood and tools? over their shoulder in their pockets

5. What shape did you picture the floor? square circle triangle

6. How many walls did you picture? _____

7. What did you see them nail the walls to? the ground the floor the sky

8. What did you see them put on top of the walls? the floor the roof

9. How many people did you picture? one two

B **Picture This:** They brought up flashlights and a radio. Then they unrolled their sleeping bags and stayed in the tree house all night.

Underline or write in the answer that best matches your own picture.

1. What did those words make you picture?   camp out in a tree house   camp out in a tent

2. What did you see them doing?   playing the radio and sleeping   building a fire

3. What did you picture them listening to?   the radio   the flashlights

4. When did you see them camping?   at night   during day

5. How did you see the flashlights?   on all night   off all night   on and off

6. What color did you picture their sleeping bags? _____

7. How did you picture their unrolled sleeping bags?   flat like a pancake   round like a ball

Picture Summary:

Put these in the right order. Draw a picture if you want.

They got their sleeping bags and spent the night there.	A man and his son built a tree house.	They brought a radio and flashlights into the tree house.

29

Word Summary:

Fill in the blanks using the words listed below.

Father and _____ took wood and tools into

a tree. They _____ a tree house. Then they

_____ in flashlights and a radio. They got

sleeping bags and stayed there all _____ .

night   **son**   **built**   **brought**

Main Idea:

Connect these with a line.

Father and son cut down a tree.	a detail
They brought in flashlights.	main idea
Father and son built a new tree house.	wrong

Spelling Practice:

Trace then cover the word.   Air-write then pencil write the word.

ladder _____ _____

built _____ _____

Vocabulary Check:

Draw a line from the word to its meaning.

father	a tool used to pound things
hammer	a metal pin with a flat, round top
nail	to carry something heavy
built	dad
haul	made

HOTS Questions:

1. Why do you think they made a tree house? _____

_____

2. Where do you think they put the door of the tree house? _____

_____

3. Why do you think the tree house needed a roof? _____

_____

4. Do you think you could sleep in the tree house? _____

_____

Vocabulary Fun:

Color the picture that best matches the word.

tree house	hammer	flashlight

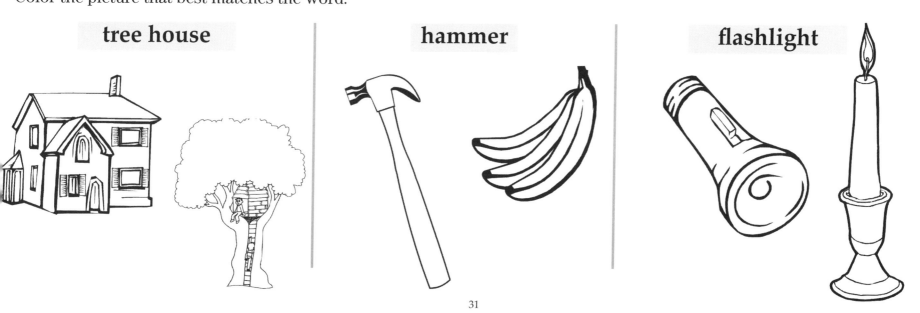

8 A Hairy Hunter

The big, brown wolf spider sneaks through the dry leaves toward the cricket. He waits for the bug to start eating a leaf. He jumps and the bug turns and looks at him. Before the bug can move, the spider lands on it and pins it down.

Vocabulary to Visualize:

wolf spider: a hairy brown spider with big teeth but no poison
sneak: to move without making a sound or being seen
cricket: a jumping bug with long legs that makes chirping noises
pin: to hold in one place

Picture This: The big, brown wolf spider sneaks through the dry leaves toward the cricket. He waits for the bug to start eating a leaf.

Underline the answer that best matches your own picture.

1. What did those words make you picture?	spider hunting bug	spider eating leaf
2. How did you see the spider hunting?	creeping toward cricket	running away from cricket
3. How did you picture him sneaking?	walking slow	running fast
4. What did you picture the spider sneaking through?	leaves	dirt
5. What color did you picture dry leaves?	purple	brown	white
6. Where did you picture this happening?	inside	outside
7. How did you picture the spider waiting?	not moving	running
8. How did you see the bug eat the leaf?	chewing on	riding on it
9. How did you picture the wolf spider's skin?	hairy	smooth

Picture This: He jumps and the bug turns and looks at him. Before the bug can move, the spider lands on it and pins it down.

Underline the answer that best matches your own picture.

1. What did those words make you picture?   spider catching bug   spider missing bug

2. How did you see the spider catch the bug?   jumped on it   ran to it   walked to it

3. What part of his body did you see him use to jump?   his eyes   his legs

4. How did you see the bug turn to look?   it faces spider   it faces the tree

5. How did you see the spider jump?   fast   slow

6. Where did you picture the spider landing?   on the cricket's back   on the cricket's belly

7. How did you picture the spider pinning it down?   holding it to ground   letting it go

Picture Summary:

Put these in the right order. Draw a picture if you want.

He jumped toward the cricket and the cricket looked at him.	The spider landed on the cricket and held it to the ground.	A big, brown spider crept toward a cricket.

Word Summary:
Fill in the blanks using the words listed below.

A wolf _____ crept toward a cricket. The

cricket started eating a _____ . The spider

_____ and the bug saw it. Before the cricket

could move, the spider _____ it.

jumped   **leaf**   **spider**   **pinned**

Main Idea:
Connect these with a line.

The wolf spider catches a cricket.		a detail
The cricket catches a wolf spider.		main idea
A cricket eats a leaf.		wrong

Spelling Practice:
Trace then cover the word.   Air-write then pencil write the word.

jump

spider

Vocabulary Check:
Draw a line from the word to its meaning.

wolf spider	a jumping bug with long legs
cricket	a hairy brown spider
pin	to move without being seen
sneak	to come down onto ground
land	to hold down

HOTS Questions:

1. What do you think will happen next? _____

_____

2. Why do you think the spider is creeping in the leaves? _____

_____

3. Why do you think the spider waits for the cricket to start eating? _____

_____

4. Why do you think the bug turns to look when the spider jumps? _____

_____

Vocabulary Fun:

Color the picture that best matches the word.

| spider | cricket | leaf |

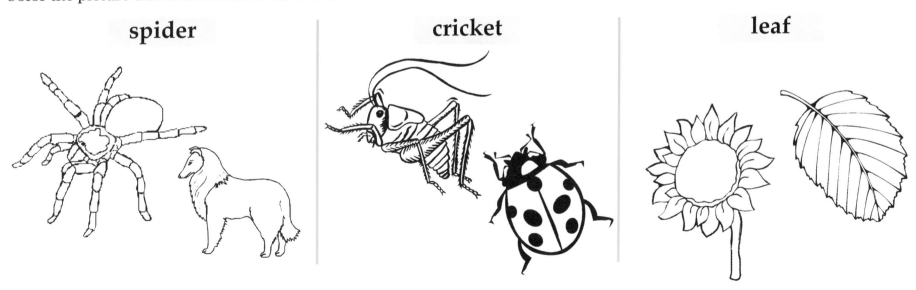

9 A Hard Meal

The furry brown sea otter eats her meals in the sea! First she dives to the sea floor to grab a rock and a hard-shelled clam. Then she floats on her back and sets the jagged rock on her chest. She holds the clam in her paws and beats its tough shell on the rock. Then the shell cracks open. Lunchtime!

Vocabulary to Visualize:

furry: being covered with short thick hair
sea otter: an animal with thick fur and webbed feet that lives in the ocean
clam: a sea animal that lives in a shell with two parts
jagged: having rough, sharp edges

Word Summary:

Fill in the blanks using the words listed below.

The _____ eats in the ocean. She goes to the bottom and gets a _____ and

a _____ . She floats on her _____ with the rock on her chest. She beats the clam against

the rock until it cracks open. Then she can eat it.

| rock | clam | sea otter | back |

Imagery Questions:

Underline the answer that best matches your own picture.

1. Where did you picture the sea otter?	in the ocean	in a puddle	in the air
2. Where did you see the rock?	on her chest	on her back	in her mouth
3. How did you see her floating?	on her back	on her belly	
4. How did you see her holding the clam?	with two hands	with one hand	in her mouth
5. What did you see the shell hitting?	her chest	the rock	her paws
6. What did you see inside the hard shell?	soft meat	water	

ain Idea:

onnect these with a line.

| he clam eats otters. |

| he sea otter eats a clam. |

| he sea otter gets a agged rock. |

a detail

main idea

wrong

Draw This:

Draw something you pictured.

OTS Questions:

. Why do you think the otter has to beat the shell on the rock? _____

_____

. Why do you think she uses a rock? _____

_____

. Why do you think she floats on her back and not her belly? _____

_____

. Why do you think the rock needs to be jagged? _____

_____

10 Stinky

A skunk can stand up to a dog, even if the dog is much larger than him. When a big dog gets too close, the skunk hisses and stamps his feet. If the dog will not leave, the skunk turns to point his rear at it. The skunk lifts his bushy tail and shoots out a stinky spray.

Vocabulary to Visualize:

skunk: small black and white animal
stamp: to pound feet up and down on the ground
bushy: furry and thick
spray: like a small fog

Word Summary:

Fill in the blanks using the words listed below.

The _____ doesn't have to run from bigger dogs. When a _____ gets too close, the skunk can warn him by hissing and stomping his feet. If the dog doesn't leave, the skunk points his_____ at it. The skunk shoots a _____ from under his tail that really stinks.

rear   **skunk**   **dog**   **spray**

Imagery Questions:

Underline or write in the answer that best matches your own picture.

1. What color did you picture the skunk? _____ and _____

2. When did you see the skunk stamp his feet?   when dog came near   when dog ran away

3. How did you see the dog too close?   near the skunk   running away from the skunk

4. What did you see the skunk do when the dog stayed?   turned rear to dog   barked at dog

5. What did you see the skunk lift to shoot his spray?   his head   his tail

6. What did you see the spray hit?   the tree   the dog

ain Idea:

onnect these with a line.

skunk can stand up to a og.		a detail
skunk hisses and stamps is feet.		main idea
dog can stand up to a kunk.		wrong

Draw This:

Draw something you pictured.

OTS Questions:

. Why do you think the dog comes near the skunk? _____

_____

. Why might the skunk stamp his feet and hiss? _____

_____

. Why do you think the skunk lifts his bushy tail? _____

_____

. Do you think this makes the skunk stinky? _____

_____

11 Escape!

The long, slimy, yellow slug inched through the leaves. A hungry shrew ran up and snatched him in her jaws. His slime numbed her tongue and gums. She dropped the slug and ran away.

Vocabulary to Visualize:

escape: to get away
slimy: wet and sticky
slug: a slimy animal with no legs
inch: to move very slowly, bit by bit
shrew: a small, mouse-like animal with a long snout
snatch: to grab
numb: having no feeling at all

Word Summary:

Fill in the blanks using the words listed below.

A slug moved through the _____ . A shrew ran up and got him in her _____ , but the

slug's _____ made her mouth numb. The shrew let the _____ go and ran away.

| mouth | slime | leaves | slug |

Imagery Questions:

Underline the answer that best matches your own picture.

1. What did you see for the slug?	a small, slimy animal	a tall green plant
2. Where did you see this happen?	in some leaves	in water
3. How did you picture the hungry shrew?	skinny	fat
4. What did you picture the shrew grabbing the slug with?	her jaws	her paws
5. What did you picture coming out of the slug?	slime	hair
6. What did you see the shrew do when her mouth went numb?	dropped the slug	ate the slug

Main Idea:

Connect these with a line.

A slug was eaten by a shrew.	a detail
The slug was slimy and yellow.	main idea
A slug escaped a shrew.	wrong

Draw This:

Draw something you pictured.

HOTS Questions:

. Why do you think the slug did not run away from the shrew?_____

_____

. Where do you think the slime came from?_____

_____

. Why do you think the shrew did not eat the slug?_____

_____

. Why do you think the slug has the slime?_____

_____

43

12 Baseball Star

The player tapped the dirt off his cleats with the end of his bat. He took three warm-up swings while he waited for his turn. He winked at the pitcher as he walked up to home plate. At the plate, he raised the bat ready to swing. He smacked the first pitch over the back fence for a homerun.

Vocabulary to Visualize:

tap: to hit something softly
cleat: a shoe with spikes on the bottom
home plate: a base with 5 sides
raise: lift up
smack: to hit really hard
pitch: a throw from the pitcher to the batter

Word Summary:

Fill in the blanks using the words listed below.

A baseball player knocked the dirt off his shoes with his _____. He took some swings to warm up.

He _____ at the pitcher when he went up to bat. He got ready to swing. He sent the first pitch over

the _____ for a _____ .

| fence | winked | homerun | bat |

Imagery Questions:

Underline the answer that best matches your own picture.

1. Where did you picture this happening?	in a baseball stadium	in the back yard
2. What did you see in the player's hands?	a bat a ball	
3. What part of his cleats did you see him tap?	the side the top	the bottom
4. How did you picture him winking?	blinked one eye	blinked both eyes
5. Where did you see him standing when he hit the ball?	next to home plate	on a chair
6. What did you see him hit the ball with?	his hand his hat	his bat

Main Idea:

Connect these with a line.

The player winked at the pitcher.	a detail
The player struck out.	main idea
The player hit a homerun.	wrong

Draw This:

Draw something you pictured.

HOTS Questions:

1. What do you think happened next? _____

_____

2. Why do you think he tapped the dirt off his cleats? _____

_____

3. Why do you think he swung the bat three times? _____

_____

4. Why do you think he winked at the pitcher? _____

_____

13 A Chubby Monster

The stout orange and black Gila monster crawls on the desert sand. He flicks out his forked tongue and smells snake eggs close by. He digs through the sand with his front claws. He finds a pile of snake eggs and bites one with his strong jaws. He chews through the tough shell and turns to the next egg.

Vocabulary to Visualize:

stout: fat
Gila monster: a fat desert lizard
flick: to move something in a light, quick way
forked: splitting near the end into two parts

Word Summary:

Fill in the blanks using the words listed below.

The Gila monster moved along the _____ . He stuck out his tongue and smelled some snake

_____ . He _____ at the sand with his front claws. When he found a pile of

_____ eggs, he ate the shells and all.

| eggs | snake | sand | dug |

Imagery Questions:

Underline or write in the answer that best matches your own picture.

| 1. What color did you see the Gila monster? _____ and _____ |
2. Where did you picture this happening?	desert	snow
3. What did you see for a pile of eggs?	eggs together	eggs spread out
4. How did you see him eat the egg?	with the shell	without the shell
5. How did you see his forked tongue?	split at end	no split
6. Where did you see him dig?	in the sand	in a tree	in water

Main Idea:

Connect these with a line.

A snake finds and eats a bunch of Gila monster eggs.	a detail
The Gila monster finds and eats a bunch of snake eggs.	main idea
The Gila monster is chubby.	wrong

Draw This:

Draw something you pictured.

HOTS Questions:

1. How do you think he knows where to dig for the eggs? _____

_____

2. Why do you think he needs front claws? _____

_____

3. Why do you think he has strong jaws? _____

_____

4. What do you think he will do next? _____

_____

14 Hungry Bear

The fat brown bear eyes the tasty berries on the bush. She puts a whole branch in her mouth and strips the fruit off with just her lips. Then she trots down to the small waterfall. While she stands next to the cold water, she catches the jumping fish in her mouth. Stuffed, she waddles to her den where she will sleep for the winter.

Vocabulary to Visualize:

eye: to stare at
trot: to run slowly
stuffed: full of food
waddle: to walk with short steps, swaying back and forth
den: the home of a wild animal
winter: the coldest season of the year

Word Summary:

Fill in the blanks using the words listed below.

A _____ saw some berries on a _____ . She stripped the berries off with her lips. Then

she went down to a waterfall to eat some _____ . When she was really full, she went to sleep for the

_____ .

fish	winter	bush	bear

Imagery Questions:

Underline the answer that best matches your own picture.

1. How did you see the bear eyeing the tasty berries?	looks at berries		looks at tree
2. Where did you see her put the branch?	in her mouth		in her paws
3. How did you see her go to the waterfall?	run	walk	fall
4. How did you see her catch the fish?	with her paws		in her mouth
5. What did you see her do with the fish she caught?	ate them		played with them
6. How did you picture that the bear was stuffed?	really fat		really skinny

Main Idea:

Connect these with a line.

The bear doesn't eat anything and then goes to sleep.		a detail
The bear eats a lot and goes to sleep for the winter.		main idea
The bear sees some tasty berries.		wrong

Draw This:

Draw something you pictured.

HOTS Questions:

1. Why do you think she eyes the tasty berries? _____

_____

2. Why do you think she trots down to the stream? _____

_____

3. Why do you think the bear is fat? _____

_____

4. Why do you think she waddles to her den instead of running? _____

_____

15 Termite

A lone termite lugs a bit of wood up a mound of dried mud. At the very top, he finds the hole and crawls in the nest. There are hundreds of termites in this nest, and he pushes his way through the crowd. He winds down through the dark tunnels. Then he drops the tasty wood and begins to eat.

Vocabulary to Visualize:

termite: a bug that eats wood
lone: one all by itself
lug: to carry something heavy
mound: a pile of dirt or mud
nest: a place where animals live
wind: to walk along a curving path

Word Summary:

Fill in the blanks using the words listed below.

A termite carried a bit of _____ up the side of the dried mud mound. He crawled into a

_____ at the top of the nest. He pushed through the many other termites and wound through the

_____ tunnels. Then he dropped the bit of tasty wood and started to _____ it.

hole   **eat**   **wood**   **dark**

Imagery Questions:

Underline the answer that best matches your own picture.

1. What did you picture for the termite nest?	a mud hill	a puddle	a bird house	
2. How did you see the termite enter the nest?	through a hole	through an elevator		
3. How did you see the nest?	empty	crowded		
4. What did the tunnels look like?	light	dark		
5. What did you see in the termite's mouth?	a little ant	a piece of dirt	a bit of wood	
6. Where did you see him eat the wood?	bottom of tunnel	top of nest		

Main Idea:

Connect these with a line.

A termite brings a bit of wood into his nest.	a detail
A termite brings a drop of water into his nest.	main idea
Termites live in crowded nests.	wrong

Draw This:

Draw something you pictured.

HOTS Questions:

1. Why do you think the termite had the bit of wood?_____

_____

2. Why does he wind down the tunnels instead of going straight?_____

_____

3. Why do you think the tunnels in the nest are dark?_____

_____

4. Do you think he shared his piece of wood?_____

_____

16 Totem Pole

The American Indian cut down a tall, straight tree with his axe. He hacked off the branches and chipped off the bark. Then he shaved it smooth. Next he carved large animal faces in it, one above the other. He painted each face bright colors. He sunk the totem pole in the ground outside the door of his lodge.

Vocabulary to Visualize:

totem pole: a special pole carved by some American Indians
hack: to cut off
carve: to cut away
sink: to put into the ground
lodge: an American Indian home often made of logs

Word Summary:

Fill in the blanks using the words listed below.

The American Indian cut down a straight _____ . He made it _____ . He carved and painted animal _____ on it. He put the totem pole outside his _____ .

smooth	lodge	faces	tree

Imagery Questions:

Underline or write in the answer that best matches your own picture.

1. What kind of tree did you see the man cut?   a straight one   a bendy one

2. What kinds of animal faces did you see him carve? _____ , _____ , and _____

3. How tall did you picture the totem pole?   like a light pole   like a pencil   like a lamp

4. What colors did you see him paint the faces? _____ and _____

5. What color did you picture his lodge? _____

6. Where did you see him sink the totem pole?   near the lodge door   at the back of the lodge

Main Idea:

Connect these with a line.

A man made a totem pole.		a detail
A man cut down a tree.		main idea
A man cut down a totem pole.		wrong

Draw This:

Draw something you pictured.

HOTS Questions:

1. Why do you think the man picked a tall, straight tree? _____

_____

2. Why do you think he hacked off the branches? _____

_____

3. Why do you think the man made the sides smooth? _____

_____

4. Why do you think he wants the totem pole outside his lodge? _____

_____

17 Duck Decoys

Paragraph 1:

The hunter carved a block of wood into the shape of a duck. He painted eyes and feathers on it. Then he made a dozen more just like it.

Vocabulary to Visualize:

decoy: a fake
hunter: someone who kills animals
carve: to cut
dozen: twelve
flock: a group of birds
duck call: a small horn that makes a noise like a duck

P₁ Word Summary:

Fill in the blanks using the words listed below.

The hunter _____ a block of wood into a duck shape. He painted eyes and _____

on it. He made a _____ more to match.

dozen   **cut**   **feathers**

Imagery Questions:

Underline or write in the answer that best matches your picture.

1. What shape did you picture the block of wood?	a square	a circle	a triangle
2. What did you see the hunter using to carve?	a knife	a toothbrush	a comb
3. What color did you see him paint the fake duck? _____			
4. How many more did you see him make?	twelve	one	four

Paragraph 2:

At the pond, he put his wooden ducks in the water and hid in the bushes. A flock of wild ducks flew past, high in the sky. The hunter blew into his duck call, making it quack. The flock turned to go meet the wooden ducks in the pond.

P₂ Word Summary:

Fill in the blanks using the words listed below.

He put his wooden ducks in the _____ and hid in the _____ . A flock of _____ flew over. The hunter used the duck call to make a fake _____ . The wild ducks turned to meet the fake ducks.

| quack | pond | bushes | ducks |

Imagery Questions:

Underline the answer that best matches your picture.

1. Where did you see the hunter put the fake ducks?   in the pond water   in the bath tub

2. What did you see hiding in the bushes?   fake ducks   wild ducks   hunter

3. What did you see the hunter blow into?   duck call   whistle   flute

4. What did you see the wild ducks do when they heard it?   flew to water   flew away from water

Vocabulary Check:

Draw a line from the word to its meaning.

| decoy | hunter | carve | dozen |

| someone who kills animals for food | twelve | a fake | to cut |

Word Summary:

Write a summary of the whole story.

Main Idea:

Connect these with a line.

| The duck hunter tricked ducks into coming to him. | A flock of ducks tricked a hunter. | The hunter blew into a duck call. |

| a detail | main idea | wrong |

HOTS Questions:

1. Why do you think the hunter used wood and not metal for the ducks? _____

_____

2. Why do you think he made so many wooden ducks? _____

_____

3. Why do you think the wild ducks flew to meet the wooden ducks? _____

_____

4. What do you think happened next? _____

_____

18 Glass Blower

Paragraph 1:

In a room behind his shop, the young glass blower opens the door of his furnace. He heats one end of a steel pipe in the fire. Then he dips it in a tub of melted glass. When he takes it out, a blob of soft glass covers the end of the pipe.

Vocabulary to Visualize:

glass blower: someone who makes things out of melted glass
furnace: an oven with a fire inside
pipe: a long tube with a hollow center
blob: a drop of something soft
sag: to droop or bend

P₁ Word Summary:

Fill in the blanks using the words listed below.

A young _____ blower opened the door of his furnace. He heated one end of his steel

_____ in the fire. Then he dipped it in some _____ glass. When he took

it out, there was a _____ of soft glass on the end.

melted	glass	blob	pipe

Imagery Questions:

Underline the answer that best matches your picture.

1. What did you picture for the furnace?	a metal oven	a bath tub
2. What did you picture for the pipe?	an empty metal tube	a plastic bag
3. How did you see the melted glass?	goopy liquid	hard and clear
4. How did you see the blob on the end?	thin like a sheet	thick like a lump

Paragraph 2:

The man blows into the cool end of the pipe. The glass is pushed by the air and forms a bubble. He turns the pipe slowly to keep the bubble from sagging as it grows. When the glass starts to get hard, he breaks it off and puts it in a hot oven that cools slowly.

P₂ Word Summary:

Fill in the blanks using the words listed below.

A man blew into the _____ end of the pipe. The hot glass formed a _____ . He slowly twisted the pipe to make sure the bubble didn't _____ . When the glass got hard he broke it off and placed it in a _____ oven that cooled it down very slowly.

bubble   sag   cool   hot

Imagery Questions:

Underline the answer that best matches your picture.

1. What did you see the man blowing into?   cool end of pipe   hot end of pipe

2. What shape did you picture for the bubble?   round   square   triangle

3. How did you see the glass blower turning the pipe?   round and round   up and down

4. How did you picture him breaking the bubble off?   smashed it on ground   gently snapped with tool

Vocabulary Check:

Draw a line from the word to its meaning.

| furnace | pipe | blob | sag |

| a long tube with a hollow center | to droop or bend | a drop of something soft | an oven with a fire inside |

61

Word Summary:

Write a summary of the whole story.

Main Idea:

Connect these with a line.

| The glass blower breaks glass with a steel pipe. | The glass blower blows into a pipe. | The glass blower uses a pipe and melted glass to make a glass bubble. |

| a detail | main idea | wrong |

HOTS Questions:

1. Why do you think the man is called a glass blower? _____

_____

2. Why do you think the glass is melted? _____

_____

3. Why do you think the glass forms a bubble? _____

_____

4. Why do you think the glass starts to get hard? _____

_____

19 The Tree Python

Paragraph 1:

The long green python sits on a jungle tree branch. His fat coils droop off both sides of the branch. He goes to sleep until the sun goes down.

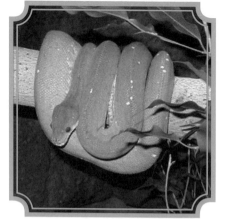

Vocabulary to Visualize:

python: a long, heavy snake that kills animals by squeezing them
coil: loops that are all connected
droop: hang down or sag
shocked: surprised

P₁

Word Summary:

Fill in the blanks using the words listed below.

The long python _____ on the tree _____ . His coils _____ off the sides of the branch. He went to sleep until the _____ went down.

sun   **drooped**   **sat**   **branch**

Imagery Questions:

Underline the answer that best matches your picture.

1. Where do you see the python sitting?   tree branch   ground   chair

2. How did you picture his coils drooping off the branch?   flat and stiff   hanging off   floating up

3. How did you picture the snake sleeping?   not moving   dancing on branch

4. How did you see that the sun went down?   sky bright   sky dark

Paragraph 2:

At night, he wakes up and sees a rabbit on the ground. When the rabbit hops under the branch, the snake slithers off and drops on his victim. He wraps around the shocked rabbit and squeezes it to death. Then he swallows it whole.

Word Summary:

Fill in the blanks using the words listed below.

The snake woke up and saw a rabbit on the _____ .

The _____ dropped onto the rabbit. The snake _____ the rabbit to death. Then he _____ the whole thing.

squeezed   **ground**   **ate**   **snake**

Imagery Questions:

Underline the answer that best matches your picture.

1. When did you see this happen?	night	morning	day
2. How did you see the snake get to the rabbit?	drop on	slither to	fly to
3. What did you see around the rabbit's body?	the snake	water	ants
4. How did you see the snake eat the rabbit?	chewed it	put it all in his mouth	

Vocabulary Check:

Draw a line from the word to its meaning.

python	shocked	coil	droop

a series of connected loops	hang down or sag	a long, heavy snake	surprised

Word Summary:

Write a summary of the whole story.

Main Idea:

Connect these with a line.

| A python catches a rabbit. | A rabbit catches a python. | A python sits on a tree branch. |

a detail   main idea   wrong

HOTS Questions:

1. Why do you think the python waited until night?_____

_____

2. What do you think the rabbit was doing?_____

_____

3. Do you think the rabbit saw the snake on the branch? Why or why not?_____

_____

4. Where do you think the snake went after he finished his meal?_____

_____

Igloo

Paragraph 1:

A man drove his dog sled across the icy plain searching for a place to build an igloo. The treeless ground stretched as far as he could see. The cold wind blew and the sun dropped low in the sky. When he found hard-packed snow, he stopped the sled.

Vocabulary to Visualize:

igloo: a dome-shaped home made out of snow
dog sled: a sled on skis pulled by dogs and steered by a person
plain: flat land with very few trees
packed: pressd tightly together; hard
huddle: to get close
dome: a round roof

P₁

Word Summary:

Fill in the blanks using the words listed below.

A man drove his dog _____ across the snow looking for a spot to build an

_____ . The _____ stretched out around him. The wind _____

and the sun went down. He stopped the sled when he found hard-packed snow.

ground	sled	blew	igloo

Imagery Questions:

Underline the answer that best matches your picture.

1. What did you picture for the dog sled?	dogs pulling sled	cats pulling sled
2. How did you picture the treeless plain?	flat, snowy ground	thick forest
3. What did you see when the wind blew?	swirling snow	blue waves
4. What did you see for hard-packed snow?	sled sinking down	sled staying on top

Paragraph 2:

The dogs huddled close as the man sawed big blocks out of the packed snow. He put the blocks in a circle on the frozen ground. Then he stacked snow blocks higher and higher, until he had a house the shape of a dome. Last, he cut in one small door, and he and the dogs crawled in.

P₂ Word Summary:

Fill in the blanks using the words listed below.

The dogs waited while the man cut big _____ of snow out of the ground. The blocks of _____ were put in a circle. He stacked them up. He cut a _____ in the igloo and they _____ crawled in.

door   **blocks**   **snow**   **all**

Imagery Questions:

Underline the answer that best matches your picture.

1. How did you picture the dogs huddling?   laying close together   spreading apart

2. Where did you see the man get the blocks of snow?   from the ground   from the trees

3. How did you see him put the blocks on the ground?   in a circle   in a square

4. What did you picture for the dome-shaped igloo?   like an upside down bowl   like a square house

Vocabulary Check:

Draw a line from the word to its meaning.

dog sled   plain   igloo   packed

flat land with very few trees   a dome-shaped snow home   a sled on skis pulled by dogs   pressed tightly together; hard

Word Summary:

Write a summary of the whole story.

Main Idea:

Connect these with a line.

A man made an igloo to get out of the cold.

The man made an igloo so he could freeze.

The dogs huddled in a circle.

a detail

main idea

wrong

HOTS Questions:

1. Why do you think he sawed blocks from packed snow and not soft snow? _____

_____

2. Why do you think he cut a small door and not a big one? _____

_____

3. What do you think might happen if he built a big fire? _____

_____

4. Why do you think the man built the igloo? _____

_____

21 Killer Whale

Paragraph 1:

Two large white-bellied orcas swim in the cold seas, looking for prey. Their big fins flash in the sun when they come up for air. They lick the back of their sharp teeth in hunger. Their strong flat tails move up and down pushing them along the hunt.

Vocabulary to Visualize:

orca: a large whale also called the "killer whale"
prey: animals that other animals kill and eat
flash: shine quickly
bob: bounce up and down on the water
gulp: swallow a large amount quickly

P₁

Word Summary:

Fill in the blanks using the words listed below.

Two _____ swam in the ocean looking for food. Their _____ popped

above the water when they came up for air. They licked the backs of their sharp_____

because they were hungry. Their _____ flapped up and down to help them swim.

| teeth | tails | orcas | fins |

Imagery Questions:

Underline or write in the answer that best matches your picture.

1. What color did you picture the orcas' bellies? _____

2. How did you see the fins flashing?   shining in the sun   staying underwater

3. What color did you picture their tongues? _____

4. How did you see their tails move?   side to side   up and down

Paragraph 2:

The orcas spot three gray seals lying on a chunk of ice bobbing on the waves. One orca swims up under the ice and bumps it with her head. As the ice tilts, the seals slip into the water. After a few strong bites, the orcas gulp the seals down.

Word Summary:

Fill in the blanks using the words listed below.

The orcas saw three _____ on a chunk of ice. One orca bumped the bottom of the ice with its _____ .

When the ice tilted, the seals slipped into the _____ .

Then the orcas _____ the seals.

ate   **seals**   **head**   **ocean**

Imagery Questions:

Underline the answer that best matches your picture.

1. What did you see for the chunk of ice?   a snowflake   a floating piece of ice

2. Where did you see the orca bump the ice?   under it   on top of it

3. How did you see the seals slip off the ice?   slid into water   held on to ice

4. What did you see the orcas eating?   the ice   the water   the seals

---

Vocabulary Check:

Draw a line from the word to its meaning.

orca   prey   flash   bob

animals that other animals eat   a large whale   bounce up and down on the water   shine quickly

Word Summary:

Write a summary of the whole story.

Main Idea:

Connect these with a line.

| Two orcas hunt seals. | Two seals hunt orcas. | Seals float on ice. |

| a detail | main idea | wrong |

HOTS Questions:

1. How do you think the orcas knew where to find the seals? _____

_____

2. How do you think the water felt? _____

_____

3. Why do you think the seals didn't get away? _____

_____

4. Why do you think the orcas hunted together? _____

_____

22 Poor Goose

Paragraph 1:

Nene geese lived on an island where they had no enemies. Flocks of the birds nested on the ground, free to feast on berries and fruit. Then one day sailors discovered the island.

Vocabulary to Visualize:

nene: (nay-nay) a small goose that lives on a tropical island
island: a piece of land that has water all around
enemy: a person or animal that hurts others
nest: a home for some animals

P1 Word Summary:

Fill in the blanks using the words listed below.

The _____ geese lived on an island where they had no enemies. They built their

nests on the _____ . They ate berries and _____ . One day, sailors

_____ to the island.

came	**nene**	**fruit**	**ground**

Imagery Questions:

Underline or write in the answer that best matches your picture.

1. What color did you picture the nene geese? _____

2. Where did you see their nests?   on the ground   in trees   in bushes

3. What did you see them eating?   berries   leaves   fish

4. How did you see the sailors get to the island?   on paper   on ships   in cars

Paragraph 2:

Hungry rats hid on the sailors' ships and snuck ashore. The rats crept from nest to nest and ate the birds' eggs. Without eggs, no new nene were born. Now there are very few nene left on the island.

P₂ **Word Summary:**
Fill in the blanks using the words listed below.

Hungry _____ snuck onto the island. They went

into each _____ and ate the eggs. No new

_____ were born. Now there are _____

nene geese left on the island.

few   **rats**   **nest**   **nene**

Imagery Questions:

Underline the answer that best matches your picture.

1. How did you picture the rats sneaking on the island?   they flew   they swam

2. What did you see the rats eating?   eggs   birds   ships

3. How did you see the number of geese changing?   more geese on island   fewer geese on island

4. How many nene do you see on the island now?   lots   very few   none

---

Vocabulary Check:

Draw a line from the word to its meaning.

| nene | island | enemy | nest |

| land with water all around | a home for some animals | a person or animal that hurts others | a small island goose |

Word Summary:

Write a summary of the whole story.

Main Idea:

Connect these with a line.

| Many nene have been killed by rats. | The nene geese have been helped by rats. | Rats snuck onto shore. |

| a detail | main idea | wrong |

HOTS Questions:

1. Why do you think the nene built their nests on the ground? _____

_____

2. Do you think the sailors brought the rats on purpose? Why or why not? _____

_____

3. Why do you think the rats ate the eggs? _____

_____

4. Can you think of a safer place for the birds to build their nests? Where? _____

_____

23 Rattler

Paragraph 1:

The tan and brown rattlesnake slid across the desert sand to a trail. She looked both ways to make sure the trail was empty before she tried to cross it. Nothing was on the trail, so off she went.

Vocabulary to Visualize:

rattlesnake: a deadly snake with a rattle at the end of its tail
sharp-hoofed: having hooves with hard edges that can cut
coil: to curl into stacked rings
fang: very sharp tooth
rear: to rise up on two legs

P1

Word Summary:

Fill in the blanks using the words listed below.

A tan and brown rattlesnake moved along the desert to a _____. She looked both

_____ to be sure it was empty. It was, so off she went to _____ the trail.

cross   **trail**   **ways**

Imagery Questions:

Underline or write in the answer that best matches your picture.

1. What colors did you see the rattlesnake? _____ and _____		
2. What did you picture for the trail?	a small path	a highway
3. How did you see the trail empty?	full of animals and cars	nothing on it
4. How did you see her cross it?	slide onto it	run away from it

Paragraph 2:

When a sharp-hoofed horse ran up the trail, the snake coiled in fear. She showed her poison-filled fangs. She shook her tail back and forth to make it rattle. When the horse heard the rattle, he reared. His neigh filled the air as he galloped away and left the snake alone.

Word Summary:

Fill in the blanks using the words listed below.

A sharp-hoofed _____ came up the trail. The scared snake coiled and showed her sharp _____.

She rattled her _____ by shaking it. The horse reared and neighed. Then he _____ away.

| ran | horse | tail | fangs |

Imagery Questions:

Underline the answer that best matches your picture.

1. How did you see the coiled snake?   stretched out   curled in stacks

2. What did you picture for sharp fangs?   pointy   flat   rounded

3. How did you see the snake rattle her tail?   bury it   shake it   keep it still

4. How did you see the horse rear?   go up on its back legs   go up on its front legs

---

Vocabulary Check:

Draw a line from the word to its meaning.

| sharp-hoofed | coil | fang | rear |

| to curl into rings | to rise up on two legs | having hooves with edges that can cut | very sharp tooth |

81

Word Summary:

Write a summary of the whole story.

Main Idea:

Connect these with a line.

| The rattlesnake scared away a horse. | The rattlesnake made friends with a horse. | The rattlesnake checked to make sure the trail was empty. |

| a detail | main idea | wrong |

HOTS Questions:

1. What do you think happened next? _____

_____

2. How do you think the horse felt? _____

_____

3. How do you think the snake felt? _____

_____

4. Why do you think the snake has a tail that rattles? _____

_____

24 Smoke Signals

Paragraph 1:

When their village was about to be attacked, some American Indian tribes made smoke signals. The smoke warned the next village of the danger. Two men built a fire with dry wood. When the flames burned hot, they tossed in damp green leaves and grass. The burning plants put out a thick gray smoke.

Vocabulary to Visualize:

signal: a sign for other people to see
village: a small town or group of people living together
damp: wet, but not soaked
puff: small cloud or gust

P₁

Word Summary:

Fill in the blanks using the words listed below.

An American Indian village was going to be attacked so they made _____ signals.

These signals warned the next village. Two men built a _____ . They threw in wet

_____ and _____ . The wet plants gave off a thick smoke.

| leaves | smoke | fire | grass |

Imagery Questions:

Underline or write in the answer that best matches your picture.

1. What did you see for the village?	tepees	skyscrapers	nests
2. What did you see the two men build?	a house	a fire	a spear
3. What color did you picture the wet plants?	green	brown	black
4. What color did you picture the thick smoke?	_____		

Paragraph 2:

The men stretched a large blanket above the fire to catch the smoke. When they flapped the blanket up and down, big puffs of smoke rose into the sky. The puffs climbed so high that they were seen by people miles away.

P₂ Word Summary:

Fill in the blanks using the words listed below.

The men pulled out a large blanket and stretched it over the

_____ . When they flapped the blanket up and down,

_____ of smoke went up in the sky. The puffs went

up so _____ , people in the next village could

_____ them.

high   **see**   **smoke**   **puffs**

Imagery Questions:

Underline the answer that best matches your picture.

1. What size did you picture the blanket?   a baby blanket   a big blanket

2. What did you see for the smoke under the blanket?   a cloud under it   nothing under it

3. What did you see the puffs do?   blow away   rise like clouds

4. Where did you see the next village?   really close   far away

Vocabulary Check:

Draw a line from the word to its meaning.

signal   puff   village   damp

wet, but not soaked   small cloud or gust   sign for people to see from far off   a small town

85

Word Summary:

Write a summary of the whole story.

Main Idea:

Connect these with a line.

| American Indians blew loud horns to warn the next village of danger. | American Indians put wet plants in fires. | American Indians made smoke signals to warn the next village of danger. |

| a detail | main idea | wrong |

HOTS Questions:

1. Why do you think they warned other villages?_____

_____

2. Why do you think they needed the blanket? _____

_____

3. What do you think the other village did when they saw the signals?_____

_____

4. What do you think they did after they sent the smoke signals?_____

_____

Notes:

Analysis of Student Performance

_____

_____

_____

_____

_____

_____

_____

_____

_____

_____

_____

_____

_____

_____